Drip, Drop, Drip!

by Janelle Cherrington
Illustrated by Maxie Chambliss

SCHOLASTIC

The  rain is here!

The cats come in.

The come out.
worms

The comes down.
rain

3

Drip, drop, drip!

He likes the .

rain

The  is here!
rain

The cats come in.

The worms come out.

The rain comes down.

5

Drop, drip, drop!

She likes the .

The is here!

The cats ran in.

We ran out.

We like the !

My Words

* come	*down	cats
* comes	*here	in
	*out	

Rr

ran

drip

-op

drop

*new high frequency words